This book belongs to

....

....

Thank you for helping Nelson by keeping our seas clean!

*For all the children who are the real Wild Tribe Heroes and continue to inspire me
by all their fantastic efforts to help our planet! EJ*

For Alfie and Freddie who are a constant source of inspiration and encourageme

First published by Under Pressure Media Ltd
Looe Cornwall PL13 1HT

Text copyright © Eleanor Jackson 2018
Illustrations copyright © Laura Callwood 2018

Printed sustainably in the UK by www.exwhyzed.co.uk

10 9 8 7 6 5 4 3 2

A CIP catalogue record for this book is available from the British Library.

ISBN 978-1-9997485-4-8

To find out more about Nelson and the other Wild Tribe Heroes, plus activities and games and how you can help, visit
www.wildtribeheroes.com or Facebook, Instagram and Twitter @wildtribeheroes.

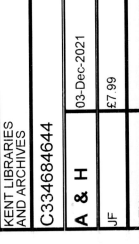

Nelson's Dangerous Dive

Story by Ellie Jackson

Illustrations by Laura Callwood

Under Pressure Media Ltd - United Kingdom

"Mayday! Mayday! Mayday! We need help quickly! Our boat is sinking in the storm!" The crew knew their old fishing boat was in urgent danger, but calmly waited for the rescue teams and helicopter to locate their flashing emergency beacon and save them.

As the crew were winched to safety they looked down and saw the heavy fishing nets pulling the back of the boat into the crashing waves. Suddenly, the bow of the boat started to rise up and the long nets began to unravel, slowly dragging the boat underwater where it settled on the rocky seabed deep below.

Over many years nature began to reclaim the boat, turning it into a magnificent reef which became home to many different sea creatures. Brightly coloured corals of all shapes and sizes grew along the rusted rails and over the decks.

Smooth gliding sharks circled the wreck chasing the fast swimming fish that darted around the wheelhouse, whilst crabs, lobsters, rays and octopus all found a home amongst the corals.

One day, a curious young whale called Nelson spied the wreck looming out of the sandy depths below. Astonished to see such a strange and colourful sight, he took a giant breath and with a flick of his impressive tail, dived deep into the shadows to see what treasures he could find.

Deeper and deeper Nelson dived as the colours around him gradually faded. Once his eyes grew accustomed to the gloom, he could see the hulk of the boat appearing beneath him, the fishing nets trailing far behind in the swirling currents looking like waving beds of seaweed.

Nelson began to explore the wreck when out of the corner of his eye he saw something flash past in the darkness. As he turned to investigate, his huge tail stretched out behind him and was captured in the nets, bringing his whole body to a shuddering stop.

Thrashing about and getting more entangled with every movement, Nelson had to use all of his determination to try to break free of the terrible ropes and nets made of plastic which bound him to the wreck.

Nelson used his immense strength to try to power through the water and the whole wreck started shifting around on the seabed as he desperately tried to escape.

Suddenly, with a loud SNAP, the rusty chains holding the ropes broke free and he found himself floating sluggishly upwards. Nelson was now almost completely entwined in the net, floating up in slow spirals until he reached the surface, finally breathing large lungfuls of fresh air.

Lying still and resting on the surface, Nelson managed to find enough strength to raise his tail and slap it down hard on the water, frantically trying to signal his need for help. Splash! Splash! Splash! The tremendous sound each tail slap created was quickly noticed by a nearby boat of tourists, who cautiously motored closer to see the commotion.

They saw Nelson's enormous and powerful body, wrapped in heavy green fishing nets and utterly powerless to free himself. He urgently needed their help if he was to survive and yet how could they help such a giant animal without risking their own lives?

Bravely the people decided they had to help. Using their boat knives they cut away the nets, one strand at a time. As each rope fell away, Nelson felt the pressure around his body start to ease and he had to fight the urge to swim away, knowing he still needed their help.

Leaning dangerously over the edge of the boat, surrounded by nets and at the mercy of the powerful whale, the people had a mammoth task ahead of them. The giant nets were so tightly wound around Nelson's body, the knives seemed to barely make a dent in their work. Yet slowly and surely the nets became looser, until finally only his enormous tail remained tangled.

Nelson's long fins were now released and realising he could swim, he started to head further out to sea, pulling the boat behind him. His rescuers were in extreme danger now should Nelson decide to dive. They had no choice but to be towed by him as he swam on, before tiring at last, he finally stopped.

Quickly now, aware of the danger they were still in, the people excitedly cut the few remaining strands of the net from around his tail and Nelson was at last completely free! As he disappeared quickly out of sight beneath them, the tourists celebrated their incredible encounter with this beautiful creature.

Suddenly, a huge shape powered up from beneath the water as Nelson burst out of the sea into the most spectacular breach. Great big splashes of glistening water cascaded down around him as his magnificent body rejoiced in its freedom. Time and again, he dived down only to swim quickly up and out of the sea in a towering spray of seawater as he showed off his powerful tail and flippers for all to see.

As Nelson swam away for the last time, the people hauled the rest of the heavy fishing net safely aboard the boat. The Captain knew that if the net was left in the water it would trap even more animals like Nelson. She thought there could be more nets down on the wreck and called the local expert diving group for help to clear them.

The team of divers arrived quickly, carrying out safety checks and surveys to work out the best way to remove the remaining nets. Fishing boats have many ropes and nets made from different types of plastic and the wreck still had several large nets tangled around it. The divers were all highly trained to remove these nets as it is very dangerous underwater work.

Using special equipment and knives, the divers cut away at the nets, sending them carefully up to the surface to be pulled into the waiting boat. Every piece of rope or net they removed would save many turtles, dolphins, seals, whales, fish, octopus, crabs and lobsters from becoming trapped over the years, and the divers felt very pleased knowing how important their work was.

As the last of the nets were brought up to the dive boat and the divers were starting to head for home, they heard an almighty splash just behind them.

Looking around quickly they saw Nelson slapping his enormous tail once more, happily leaping out of the sea with his new friend in a spectacular and rare double breach. He was finally free of the nets that had been lost at sea, free to breach and dive, to swim and explore once again.

Did you know..?

There are about 90 different kinds of whale divided into two types. Baleen whales like Nelson have hard strong plates in their jaws made of keratin - this is the same material as your hair and fingernails. The baleen plate acts like a sieve and traps all the tiny krill they feed on. Toothed whales such as narwhal and pilot whales have teeth and feed on fish and plants.

The Blue Whale is the largest animal that has ever lived, even bigger than a dinosaur. It can grow up to 30m long and weigh up to 136 tonnes. Its heart is as big as a small car and you could fit 50 people standing on its tongue!

Whales are mammals which mean they have to come to the surface every few minutes to breathe air, although the sperm whale can hold its breath for 90 minutes. The world record for a human holding their breath underwater is 24 minutes!

Whales swim by moving their tails up and down and using their fins to turn. Some whales can swim more than 50 km/h if they are in danger but most swim about as fast as a dog can run.

When whales sleep, they shut down half of their brain and stay near the surface with their blowhole above the water. Whilst one half of the brain sleeps, the other half makes sure the whale keeps breathing air whilst resting or slowly swimming.

All whales are very noisy. They talk to each other using squeaks, groans and sighs. Whales are the loudest animals in the world. Their underwater sounds can travel great distances, sometimes as far as 6,000km - from one side of an ocean to the other!

Be a **Wild Tribe Hero** and help **stop plastic** in our **oceans!**

- Use less plastic – stop using single use plastic such as drinking straws and plastic bags – bring your own bags to the shops and say no to plastic straws.
- Stop buying bottled water – carry a reusable bottle.
- Recycle your rubbish at home and at school.
- Go plastic free for your school lunch box.
- Pick up litter you see around you if safe to do so.
- Report injured wildlife to a local charity or vets.
- Tell other people about the problem with plastics in the oceans and help spread the word by making posters and writing letters to save marine wildlife like Nelson.

YOUR actions WILL make a difference!

Please share this book and its important message with your family, friends and teachers.

What are Ghost Fishing Nets?

The nets that trapped Nelson are called Ghost Fishing Nets. These are fishing nets which have been lost or abandoned at sea. This is a huge problem in our oceans as many nets are made using plastic rope instead of natural rope. This means they are now stronger and last much longer - maybe hundreds of years.

Nets and other fishing gear can trap animals like whales, sharks, dolphins and turtles as well as fish, crabs and lobsters and they will keep on doing this for as long as the net lasts. They are called ghost nets as they keep catching animals long after they have stopped being used by fishing boats.

What can be done?

Lost or found nets can be reported to the Global Ghost Gear Initiative so they can be brought back to land to recycle the plastic into something new like clothing, carpets or even kayaks!

If you are fishing or crabbing, make sure you collect all fishing lines, nets, hooks, weights and bait nets to reuse or dispose of correctly in the bin or take home.

Fishing nets and pots should be tagged with the owner's name and a tracker so they can be returned safely.

Special bins at harbours and ports can collect nets that have been found at sea by fishermen.

By collecting or reporting any fishing nets, pots or line that you find on the beach you are keeping our oceans clean of plastic and helping our animals to stay healthy.

By choosing to eat fish that have been caught locally to you using *line caught fish* or *pot caught shellfish* you are helping to support sustainable fishing.

More True Wild Tribe Heroes Adventures

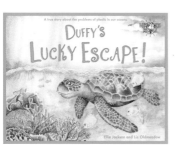

Learning about the problems of ocean plastic

Duffy's Lucky Escape will transport you to a tropical paradise where Duffy the Sea Turtle lives amongst beautiful coral reefs and colourful fish, only for Duffy to learn that all that floats is not food.

Exploring the issues of palm oil and climate change

Buddy's Rainforest Rescue sees Buddy the Orangutan living peacefully in the tangle of tall trees when he suddenly encounters the diggers destroying his magnificent rainforest home.

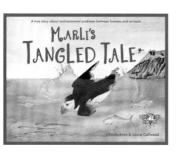

Discovering the issues around balloon releases

Marli's Tangled Tale takes you to the cool and green cliffs where Marli the Puffin lives with her soon to hatch egg, until one day the excitement of the far away town visits in an unexpected way.

Learning about bushfires and climate change

Sunny's Blazing Battle takes you to the heat of the Australian bush when a sudden fire threatens Sunny the Koala and her treetop home. Brave firefighters and kind people battle to save the little koalas before they feel safe at last.

Learning about the problem of climate change

Hunter's Icy Adventure explores the Arctic home of Hunter the Polar Bear, yet as the ice starts to melt he finds himself in a tricky situation. As help comes from high above, Hunter is in a race against time to get back to the ice.

Looking at the problem of habitat loss

Ziggy's Frightening Flight sees Ziggy the honey bee happily buzzing from flower to flower yet as time goes on she realises the flowers she loves are making her sick. Can the farmer and his children save the bees before it is too late?

Learn about the issues surrounding plastic pollution, balloon releases, ghost fishing nets, deforestation, climate change and habitat loss. All books have excellent free digital teaching resources and curriculum maps. To find out more visit: www.wildtribeheroes.com

How you can help Nelson and his friends!

One way you can help to protect our marine wildlife like whales is to pick up litter when you see it, as every piece of rubbish could end up in our seas. This can be as simple as collecting litter you see on the beach or in the park or you can ask your school or club to organise a clean up event. Millions of children around the world are doing this fun and free activity to help save our animals and you never know what things you might find! There are some things you need to do before you pick up rubbish to keep yourself safe:

1. Always go with an adult.

2. Never pick up anything that looks nasty or is dangerous.

3. Wear protective gloves and bring a bag to put rubbish in.

4. Watch out for and don't touch sharp items like glass, needles or metal.

5. BE SAFE NEAR WATER – Always follow safety signs. Look out for big waves, tide coming in or quick sand/mudflats. Be careful on the beach and near rivers, lakes and canals.

6. Keep an eye on the weather and wear appropriate clothing and sun protection.

7. Take a picture and upload it to social media using the hashtags #wildtribeheroes, #2minutebeachclean and #minibeachclean.

8. Put the rubbish in a bin or take it home to recycle/upcycle.